DOMINOES

Jake's Parrot

LEVEL ONE   **400 HEADWORDS**

OXFORD
UNIVERSITY PRESS

Great Clarendon Street, Oxford, OX2 6DP, United Kingdom

Oxford University Press is a department of the University of Oxford.
It furthers the University's objective of excellence in research, scholarship,
and education by publishing worldwide. Oxford is a registered trade
mark of Oxford University Press in the UK and in certain other countries

First published in Dominoes 2011

2025 2024 2023 2022

17

No unauthorized photocopying

ISBN: 978 0 19 424773 3   Book
ISBN: 978 0 19 463941 5   Book and Audio Pack
Audio not available separately

Printed in China

This book is printed on paper from certified and well-managed sources

ACKNOWLEDGEMENTS

Illustrations by: Gavin Reece

Cover image by: Photodisc courtesy of Getty Images

The publisher would like to thank the following for permission to reproduce photographs: Alamy pp. 6
(Peter Muhly/AFP), 18 (Alex Stokes), 25 (Design Pics Inc), 38 (John Redmond); Getty pp. 7
(pawel.gaul/E+), 19 (Doram/iStock Editorial), 40 (Kadir Barcindi/iStockPhoto).

DOMINOES

Series Editors: Bill Bowler and Sue Parminter

Jake's Parrot

Paul Hearn and Yetis Ozkan
Retold by John Escott

Illustrated by Gavin Reece

Yetis Ozkan worked as a teacher of English for more than ten years before taking up his present position as educational consultant. He is especially interested in storytelling and creative writing and has given many seminars and workshops on this subject.

Paul Hearn has been a teacher of English and foreign languages since 1995. He has worked in many countries, including Germany, Russia, and Saudi Arabia. He has taught at all levels and is currently employed at a college in Istanbul, Turkey, where he teaches teenage learners reading and writing lessons.

OXFORD
UNIVERSITY PRESS

BEFORE READING

1 **Here are some of the characters in *Jake's Parrot*. Match each sentence with a number in one of the pictures.**

a Aidan is the office boy at BananaTech Ireland. He makes tea and coffee for all the people in the office there.

b Al is Jake's friend from the United States. His father is ill.

c Arto Sneck is the director of Snecksoft, a Finnish computer game company. He is very interested in Jake's newest game.

d Brigid is the office manager at BananaTech, Ireland. She likes Jake.

e Jake Stevens writes computer games for BananaTech. He comes from the United States to Ireland for a time.

f Percy is Al's parrot. Al leaves him with Jake. Percy likes talking.

g Tomás is the director of BananaTech Ireland. He isn't very nice to Aidan.

2 **Answer these questions. What do you think?**

a Who steals Jake's laptop in the story? Why?

b Which characters help Jake to find it again?

CHAPTER 1 - DINNER FOR ONE

Jake Stevens felt excited.

The plane came down and he looked out of the window. So this was Dublin Airport.

'Goodbye Californian sun. Hello Irish rain,' he thought.

It was warm and the sky was blue when he left his San Francisco home that

December morning. Here the sky was dark and cold. But Jake felt good.

He was a writer and he worked for the American computer **company** BananaTech, in San Francisco. He was in Ireland because the people at BananaTech in Dublin needed help with the company's newest computer **game**. Jake was the writer of the game, so he knew all about it, of course.

Thirty minutes later, he was in the airport building.

An old friend met him there.

company a group of people all working to make or do something for money

game something that you play; tennis and football are games

'Hi, Al!' said Jake. Al once worked in the California office, but now he worked in Dublin.

'Hi, Jake!' answered Al. 'How are you doing?'

'OK,' Jake told him.

Then Jake saw someone with Al – a very pretty girl. His smile was suddenly bigger. 'Who's this?' he asked.

'Brigid,' Al said. 'She works in the office here.'

'Hi, Brigid,' said Jake.

'Hello, Jake,' answered Brigid. She had a nice smile.

'Hmm,' Jake thought, 'it's my first time in Ireland, but I like it here!' Then he saw Al's bag.

'Are you going away?' he asked.

'Yes. I wanted to tell you before, but I had no time,' said Al. 'I'm taking the next plane to Los Angeles.'

'Los Angeles!' said Jake. 'But why?'

'My dad's in hospital now. He's very ill,' said Al. 'And I need to go and see him.'

'Oh!' said Jake. 'I'm sorry, I – '

'So you're going to do the **presentation** for your game at the Irish Computer **Exhibition**, not me,' said Al.

'Oh, OK,' said Jake. 'But – '

'Look, I'm sorry,' said Al. 'I must go now. My plane leaves very soon. Brigid can tell you everything. See you!'

'See you!' said Jake. Al walked away, and Jake watched him. Then Jake looked at Brigid. 'What now?' he asked.

'Let's take a taxi into town,' she said. 'You're going to stay at Al's **apartment**.'

'Oh, right,' said Jake. He smiled. 'Perhaps we can have dinner later.'

She smiled back. 'Perhaps,' she said.

The taxi took them down a long, **busy** road to the **city**.

presentation a talk about something

exhibition a place where people go to see things

apartment a number of rooms in a building where someone lives

busy with lots of cars; with lots to do; with lots of people in

city (*plural* **cities**) a big and important town

After about twenty minutes, they arrived at a **place** with lots of **modern** buildings. Jake was surprised. 'So not all the buildings in Dublin are old,' he thought.

'Lots of big companies have their offices here,' said Brigid. 'BananaTech is here, and Al's apartment is very near, too.'

Brigid talked about the Dublin office of BananaTech.

'Tomás is the **director** of BananaTech Ireland. He's OK. Then there's Michael, Oona and Erin.

They can answer any of your questions when I'm not there. We've also got an office boy, Aidan. He loves computers, but he's very young. Everyone is very friendly.'

'They can't be friendlier than you,' said Jake. 'Or prettier,' he thought.

Some minutes later, they stopped in front of a very tall building. 'Al lives here,' said Brigid. 'It's BananaTech's apartment. You have this **key**, and I have one at the office.'

'OK,' said Jake.

They went up to the eighth **floor**.

The apartment was nice, and very modern. There were

place where something is

modern new (of a building or apartment)

director the most important person in a company who decides what everybody there must do

key you can close or open a door with this

floor the place in a room where you stand and walk

pictures on the white **walls**. Nearly all of them were photographs of Dublin. The chairs were black and white, and there was a TV on a little table, and a bigger table near the window.

Jake walked across to the window and looked out.

'Wonderful,' he said. 'I can see the sea!' It was grey and cold – very different from the blue Californian sea.

'Arraaaggghhhh!' **squawked** something.

Jake looked across the room quickly. 'What was that?' he asked.

wall the side of a room

squawk to make a loud noise (of a bird); a loud noise that a bird makes

4

Brigid smiled. 'That's Percy,' she said. She walked across to a tall table. There was a **cage** on the table, and a beautiful green and yellow **bird** in the cage.

'Say hello to Percy,' laughed Brigid. 'He's Al's **parrot**.'

'Parrot!' squawked the bird. 'Al's parrot!'

'He comes from Brazil,' said Brigid. 'Al's teaching him to talk.'

'Oh,' said Jake. 'Well, I like birds. So that's OK. Hi, Percy.'

'Percy!' squawked the bird.

'His **food** is in the little bottle next to the cage,' said Brigid. 'Remember to give him food and water every day.' She went to the door. 'The office is two minutes from here, so I can come for you tomorrow at nine o'clock and we can walk to work.'

'OK,' said Jake. 'But what about dinner? We can find a quiet little restaurant, and you can tell me– '

She smiled. 'Not tonight,' she said. 'Al left some food for you in the kitchen.'

'Then what about tomorrow night?' asked Jake.

Brigid laughed. 'Perhaps. See you in the morning.'

'OK,' he said.

After she left, Jake smiled and walked across to the cage. 'I like Brigid,' he said to the parrot. 'But it's dinner for one tonight, Percy. And first I must give you some dinner.'

Jake gave some food and water to the bird. Then he went and ate his dinner in the kitchen, and after that he went to bed in his room. He slept at once, and didn't hear Percy in the front room.

'Like Brigid! Like Brigid!' squawked the bird. 'Dinner for one!'

OoOoO

cage an open box to put animals or birds in

bird an animal that can fly through the sky

parrot a bird that people can teach to speak

food you eat this

READING CHECK

Choose the correct words to complete the sentences.

a Jake Stevens comes from *California/New York*.

b He writes *books/computer games*.

c He's coming to work at BananaTech *Scotland/Ireland*.

d *Al/Brigid* is an old American friend of Jake's.

e Al must go back to Los Angeles because his *mother/father* is very ill in hospital there.

f Brigid and Jake take a *taxi/train* from Dublin airport to the city.

g Brigid takes Jake to the BananaTech *offices/apartment*.

h There are photogaphs of *Dublin/Edinburgh* on the walls there.

i Jake gives some food and water to Percy, and then he has *his dinner/a drink*.

j Brigid *has/doesn't have* dinner with Jake.

WORD WORK

Use the pairs of words in the plane to complete the sentences on page 7.

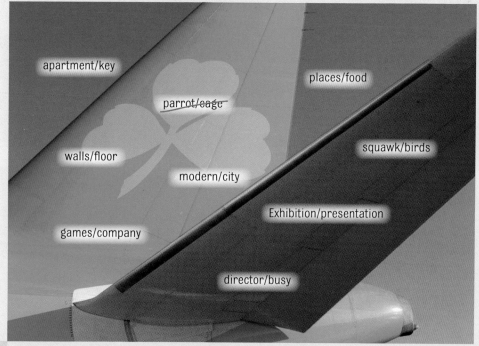

apartment/key

places/food

parrot/cage

walls/floor

squawk/birds

modern/city

Exhibition/presentation

games/company

director/busy

a Percy is a yellow and green ...parrot.... . He lives in a .....cage...... .

b Dublin is an interesting................... . Some of it is very................... .

c BananaTech is an American................... . It makes computer................... .

d Brigid has a...................to Jake's................... .

e Al can't do the...................of BananaTech's new computer game at the Irish
Computer................... .

f Tomás O'Neill is a...................man. He's the...................of BananaTech Ireland.

g My brother's room has yellow...................and a black................... .

h Where are the best...................to eat Irish...................near here?

i Some...................can't talk, they can only................... .

GUESS WHAT

What happens in the next chapter? Tick five boxes.

a Percy the parrot dies suddenly. ☐

b Brigid arrives at Jake's apartment the next morning. ☐

c Brigid walks with Jake to the BananaTech offices. ☐

d Jake and Brigid take a taxi to the BananaTech offices. ☐

e Jake says nothing to Brigid before they arrive at the office. ☐

f Jake meets Tomás, Michael, Erin, Oona, and Aidan at the office. ☐

g Brigid eats with Jake at a place near the office. ☐

h Al phones Jake from America. ☐

Dublin

7

CHAPTER 2 - BEAUTIFUL BRIGID

The next day was warm. Brigid arrived at nine o'clock. Jake was happy. 'Thanks for coming for me,' he said.

'Oh, I walk past this building every morning. It's not a **problem**.' Her face was very red, but she smiled.

So they walked to the BananaTech office and Jake talked about his work in America.

The BananaTech offices were on the twelfth floor of a tall building. Tomás, the BananaTech Ireland director, was there to say hello to them.

'Good to meet you, Jake,' he said. 'Al talks a lot about you. We want to see your new game. It's very good, Al says.'

Jake met everyone in the office – Michael, Erin, Oona and Aidan. Only Aidan did not smile when he said hello.

'We can all meet now. We need to talk about the computer exhibition,' said Tomás. 'Aidan, bring some coffee, please.'

Aidan said nothing. He walked away, his head down.

Tomás took Jake through the office to a different room. In this room there were eight chairs and a big **screen** on the wall. Everyone sat down, and Jake opened his **laptop**. Minutes later, Aidan came in with the coffee.

'Look at that! You forgot the **biscuits** again!' Tomás told him. 'Can you bring them now, please?'

Aidan did not answer. He walked out of the room.

'He always forgets the biscuits,' said Tomás. 'He's **clever**, but he's very young. He must do more office work before he begins making any computer games. Now, Jake, let's look at your new game.'

It was an exciting car **racing** game.

'Al was right. It's very good!' said Michael.

problem something difficult

screen something flat and white that you can see a presentation on

laptop a computer that you can carry with you

biscuit a little flat hard cake

clever quick-thinking

racing when there are competitions to see which car is the fastest

'I love the cars,' said Brigid. 'They're wonderful.'

'I like the **music** and **sound effects**,' said Oona.

'It's going to be the best game at the Irish Computer Exhibition,' said Tomás.

'Is it?' asked Jake.

'Of course,' said Tomás.

'Better than Snecksoft's games,' said Brigid.

'You're very clever, Jake,' said Oona.

Aidan brought the biscuits in just then, and he heard all this. He walked angrily out of the room again.

When it was time for **lunch**, Brigid took Jake to a **restaurant** near the office.

They waited for their food and Jake talked.

'When did you begin working with BananaTech?' he asked Brigid.

'Two years ago,' she answered. 'I like it there. Everyone's very friendly.'

'Aidan doesn't smile very much,' said Jake. 'Does he like working there?'

'No, he doesn't,' answered Brigid. 'He's always angry. Aidan wants to work on computer games, but he's not ready for that, you see.'

'What must happen before Aidan can work on some computer games?' asked Jake.

music people listen to this nice sound that goes with a computer game

sound effects noises of things happening in a computer game

lunch when you eat in the middle of the day

restaurant a place where people go to have things to eat

'He needs somebody to help him,' said Brigid. 'He loves computer games, but he's sixteen years old, so he needs to be an office boy a little longer. He learns quickly, but there's nobody to help him. Nobody has time.'

'Where does Aidan live?' asked Jake.

'With his family near the airport,' said Brigid. 'They don't have a lot of money, and Aidan's mum's very ill. So Aidan wants to make computer games and **become** rich and famous.'

Then the food arrived, and Jake and Brigid forgot about Aidan and his problems.

'This is wonderful!' said Jake, after a minute or two. 'I like Irish food!'

Brigid laughed. 'Well, **pizza** isn't Irish, but the **seafood** on it came from the sea near Dublin.'

Jake went red. Brigid laughed again.

'What about this evening? Would you like to come to dinner with me?' Jake asked.

She smiled, but said, 'Sorry, I can't. Not tonight.'

'Why does she always say no?' thought Jake.

That afternoon, Jake worked on his presentation for the Computer Exhibition.

At seven o'clock in the evening, there was a phone call for him. It was Al, from America.

'Hi, Jake,' he said. 'How's everything?'

'OK,' said Jake. 'What time is it there?'

'Eleven o'clock in the morning,' said Al.

'How's your dad?' asked Jake.

'He's very ill,' said Al. 'I can't come back to Dublin for some time. Perhaps not for some months. Dad is going to need help when he leaves hospital. My mum's dead, and I

become (*past* **became**) to begin to be

pizza a round, flat, hard bread from Italy cooked with cheese and tomato on it

seafood different kinds of sea fish that are soft, but have hard shells on them

don't have any brothers or sisters. I'm his only child.'

'I understand,' said Jake.

'Perhaps you can stay in Dublin for longer,' said Al. 'For four or five months. I can do your **job** in the San Francisco office. You can do my job in Dublin. You must ask Brigid about that.'

'Brigid? Not Tomás? But why?' said Jake.

'Because Brigid's the Dublin office **manager**, so she's your **boss**.'

'Oh, no!' thought Jake. 'Brigid's the office manager, and my boss. I asked my boss out to dinner!'

Then he thought, 'But after four or five months she's not going to be my boss. I'm going to ask her out to dinner again. And perhaps one day she's going to say yes!'

'Perhaps I can stay,' he said to Al. 'But let's not tell Brigid now. I want to think about it.'

'OK. Well, have a good time at the exhibition,' said Al. 'Goodbye now, Jake.'

'Goodbye, Al,' said Jake, and he put the phone down. 'And hello, beautiful Brigid!'

'Beautiful Brigid!' squawked Percy.

job work

manager a person who organizes the work of other people

boss the person that you work for

ACTIVITIES

READING CHECK

Complete the sentences with the correct names.

| Aidan | Al | Brigid | Jake | Tomás |

a At nine o'clock in the morning, ... Brigid ..... comes for .... at his apartment.

b ...., Michael, Erin, Oona and .... meet them at the office.

c '.................. talks a lot about you and your exciting new game,' says ....

d .... is very angry when .... comes in with the coffee.

e .... likes the cars in ....'s new computer game.

f .... doesn't like it when everybody says nice things to ....

g .... and .... eat near the office.

h '.................. wants to write computer games for money,' .... says before the food arrives.

i .... phones .... in the evening and says, 'I can't come back to Dublin for some months.'

WORD WORK

1 Use the letters in the cars to make words and complete the sentences.

a Aidan is .... clever ...., but he's very young. &= **relcev**

b Aidan comes into the room with coffee for everybody, but he forgets the .... &= **citsibus**

c Aidan's mother is ill, and his family don't have a lot of money. He has many .... &= **bresplom**

d Aidan wants to make computer games and .... rich and famous. &= **ebomec**

e Brigid has .... with Jake, but not dinner. &= **chunl**

f They go to a .... not far from work. &= **teturnrasa**

g Jake likes eating his .... &= **izazp**

h It has .... on the top – from the sea near Dublin.   **odefaso**

i Al wants to do Jake's .... in California.   **boj**

j Brigid is the office .... at BananaTech Ireland.   **ragamen**

k Jake is asking his .... out to dinner.   **sosb**

2 Complete Oona's notes about Jake's new computer game with other new words from Chapter 2.

> Jake Stevens's new game
> - Jake has his new game on his a) ....laptop....
> - We saw Jake's presentation about it on the big b) .... when we met today.
> - It's a car c) .... game.
> - The d) .... is nice to listen to, and the e) .... are very good, too!

GUESS WHAT

What happens in the next chapter? Tick the boxes.

1 Jake...

   a tells Brigid about Al's phone call. ☐

   b asks Brigid out to dinner again. ☐

   c forgets to give Percy the parrot food and water. ☐

2 Aidan...

   a watches Jake when he's working on his computer game. ☐

   b works on the game when Jake isn't there. ☐

   c forgets the milk in Tomás's coffee. ☐

3 Brigid...

   a eats dinner at a restaurant with Jake. ☐

   b asks Jake to dinner at her mother's house. ☐

   c meets everybody from the office at Jake's apartment. ☐

13

CHAPTER 3 - HAPPY BIRTHDAY

Jake said nothing about Al's **plan** to Brigid at the office. 'I can ask her about it at dinner this evening,' he thought. 'Can you come to dinner with me tonight?' he said to her.

'Sorry, I can't,' said Brigid. 'I'm going to have dinner at my mum's house.'

'Then what about tomorrow?' said Jake. 'You must come then. It's my **birthday**, you see. You can bring your mother!'

Brigid laughed. 'My mum doesn't like coming in to Dublin. She lives nearly sixty kilometres from here,' she said. Then she looked at him. 'But is it true? *Is* it your birthday tomorrow?'

'Yes,' said Jake, 'it is. So you must come – with or without your mother!'

'Perhaps,' said Brigid.

Next morning at the office, Brigid came to Jake's **desk**. 'Happy birthday, Jake!' she said.

'Thanks,' he answered. 'So are you coming out to dinner with me this evening?'

Brigid smiled. 'Yes. OK,' she said.

'Wonderful!' smiled Jake. 'She said "yes" to me in the end!' he thought.

'I can come for you at your apartment at seven o'clock,' said Brigid. 'I know a good restaurant near there.'

'That's wonderful,' said Jake again. 'This is going to be my best birthday.'

Jake waited for everyone in the office to say 'Happy birthday' to him, but they didn't.

'Brigid didn't tell them,' he thought.

He worked on his computer game all day. He made some

plan when you get something ready to do later; to get something ready to do later

birthday the day when someone was born

desk a table in an office

of the cars bigger and he changed some of the colours.
Aidan often came and watched him.

'Do you want faster cars, too? I can help you to do that,'
said Aidan.

'OK, Aidan,' said Jake, and he gave his chair to Aidan.

Aidan sat down and began working. After some minutes,
the cars were faster. Jake smiled. 'That's very good, Aidan.
You're clever with computers.'

Aidan smiled, but just then Tomás called from his office.
'I'd like a cup of coffee, Aidan. And don't forget the biscuits
this time!' Aidan stopped smiling, and he stood up and
walked away angrily.

Aidan took the coffee to Tomás's desk.

'Did you remember the milk?' said Tomás. 'I like a lot of
milk, you know.'

'Yes,' said Aidan. 'I know.'

He walked back to his desk and he sat down. He was angry and he didn't want to do any work. He looked across the office, but nobody looked back at him. Everybody was busy. 'This is a good time to do it,' he thought.

Aidan took a computer **magazine** from his desk. There was a picture of a man on the front of the magazine. The man was Arto Sneck, the director of Snecksoft, the Finnish computer company. **Inside** the magazine, there was some **information** about him.

Aidan read it interestedly:

'Mr Sneck is taking Snecksoft's new computer football game to the Dublin Computer Exhibition . . .'

Aidan smiled and put the magazine back on his desk.

'I'm never going to make coffee for Tomás, or any of them, again,' he thought. 'I'm going to make computer games, become rich, and help my mum to be well again.'

OoOoO

That evening, Jake couldn't stop looking at his watch. He was excited about seeing Brigid.

She arrived at the apartment at seven o'clock. She smiled when Jake opened the door to her. 'She's beautiful!' thought Jake.

'Where are we going?' he asked.

'Not far,' said Brigid.

They walked down the road by the river for five minutes. Then Brigid said, 'That's the restaurant there. Oh, no! It's

magazine a thin book with lots of pictures in it; you can buy it every week or every month

inside in

information facts

very busy tonight. Lots of people are waiting to go in.'

'Are there any more restaurants near here?' asked Jake.

'Yes, but it's Thursday night,' said Brigid. 'I'm sorry. I didn't think. All the restaurants in the city are busy on Thursday. Perhaps we can go back to your apartment and phone for a pizza.'

'Yes, OK,' said Jake.

They walked back to the apartment. Jake opened the door and they went in. The room was dark. 'We need some **light**,' said Jake, and he went over to the light by the door . . .

'Happy birthday!' **shouted** everyone suddenly, and they all **clapped**.

Jake's mouth opened. 'What . . .?!'

In the light he could see them all. Everyone was there – Tomás, Erin, Oona, and Aidan. There were lots of things to eat and drink on the table.

Jake looked at Brigid. She laughed.

'You knew!' he said.

'Of course,' she answered. 'Let's have **fun**!' she shouted to everyone.

'Happy birthday. Have fun!' squawked Percy.

light this stops a place being dark; a thing that helps you to see in the dark

shout to say noisily

clap to hit your hands together many times to show that you are pleased

fun something that you like doing

READING CHECK

Correct the mistakes in these sentences.

a Brigid is going to have dinner at her ~~dad's~~ *mum* house.

b Brigid says 'no' when Jake asks her out to dinner on his birthday.

c Everybody says 'Happy birthday!' to Jake in the office that morning.

d Michael helps Jake work on his computer game.

e Aidan forgets the milk in Tomás's coffee, and the biscuits too.

f Aidan reads a magazine with a picture of Tomás O'Neill on it.

g Brigid cries when she comes to Jake's apartment in the evening.

h All the restaurants in Dublin are busy on Monday night.

i When they go back to Jake's apartment, nobody from the office is there.

j They say 'Happy New Year!' to Jake very noisily.

WORD WORK

Use the words in the laptop to complete the sentences on page 19.

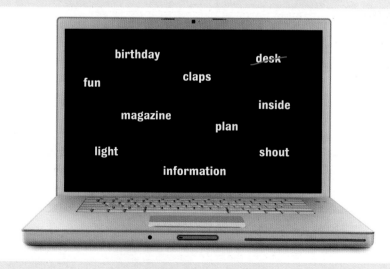

birthday   ~~desk~~

fun   claps

inside

magazine   plan

light   shout

information

a Brigid comes and speaks to Jake when he's sitting at his ......desk...... in the office. He doesn't tell her about Al's ....

b Aidan is looking at a computer .... There's .... about the Snecksoft company in it.

c Jake asks Brigid out to dinner on his ...., but the restaurant is busy, so they walk back to his apartment and go ....

d In the ...., they suddenly see everyone from the office there. They all .... 'Happy birthday!' happily.

e Everyone ...., and Brigid says to them all, 'Let's have ....!'

GUESS WHAT

What happens in the next chapter? Tick three boxes.

a Different people from the office give Jake things for his birthday. ☐

b Aidan has no money and so gives nothing to Jake. ☐

c Oona is very interested in Jake's laptop. ☐

d The next day, Tomás asks everybody in the office to dinner at his house near the River Liffey. ☐

e Michael takes Brigid's key to Jake's apartment from her desk. ☐

f Aidan phones Arto Sneck with some information. ☐

g Jake tells Brigid about the plan for him to stay in Ireland and do Al's job. ☐

h Erin goes to Jake's apartment and takes the laptop and the parrot from it. ☐

Everyone came to Jake and said, 'Happy Birthday!', and gave a **present** to him. Tomás gave Jake an old black-and-white photograph of Dublin. Erin and Oona gave him a Dublin football shirt, and Brigid gave him a beautiful hat.

'Happy birthday, Jake,' said Aidan quietly, and he gave something to Jake. Jake opened it quickly. It was a computer book – and a very good one.

'Thanks!' said Jake. 'What a wonderful book!'

'It isn't new,' said Aidan quickly. 'I read it last month. I didn't have any money for a present.'

'That isn't important,' said Jake. 'You didn't need to give a present to me, so thank you for the book.'

After that, they all began to eat the food. And they laughed and talked happily. But Aidan didn't eat. He stood and looked at Jake's laptop. It was on a little table near the window.

When it was time for everyone to go, Brigid was the last to leave the apartment.

'That was fun,' she said.

'Let's have dinner tomorrow night,' Jake told her. 'You and me. Dinner for two.'

present
something that you give to someone on their birthday

Brigid laughed. 'OK,' she said.

OoOoO

Next morning, everyone went to the office early. Jake needed to finish some things in the game, and everyone needed to make everything ready for the Computer Exhibition the next day.

Jake worked at his desk. Tomás, Aidan, and Brigid came and watched him. Jake was very busy. He needed to change some things in his computer game before the exhibition.

'I'm going to work on my laptop at the apartment this afternoon,' said Jake. 'It's quiet there – when Percy isn't talking, of course.'

'Last year Snecksoft **won** the 'Game of the Year' **prize**,' said Aidan.

'This year, BananaTech's going to win it,' said Tomás. 'And to say good luck and thank you, I'd like to take everyone in the office out to dinner this evening. There's a wonderful place in Dublin not far from the River Liffey. I'd like you to see it, Jake. There are lots of restaurants there.'

'Erm, thanks,' said Jake. 'So no dinner for two – again,' he thought. 'Are you going to come, Aidan?' he asked the office boy.

'I can't,' said Aidan quickly. 'I'm busy this evening.'

Brigid smiled and said, 'You have something more important to do than come to dinner with us?'

Tomás said, 'Well, you're not busy now. Go and make some coffee for us all, and don't forget–'

'The biscuits,' said Aidan. 'Soon you're not going to be my boss,' he thought. Aidan looked at Jake, Tomás and Brigid. They were busy. Everyone was busy. Aidan had only two or three minutes, he knew. It was now or never. Nobody saw him when he went into Brigid's office. Nobody saw him when he opened her desk. And nobody saw him

win (*past* **won**) to be the best in a competition

prize something that people give you when you are the best in a competition

when he took a key from it – the key to Jake's apartment. After that, he brought some coffee and biscuits to Jake.

'Here you are,' he smiled. 'Good luck with the game.'

When it was time for lunch, Aidan took the computer magazine from his desk and went out. He walked a hundred metres down the street from the office. Then he took his **mobile phone** from his coat pocket. He looked inside the magazine for a phone number, and he quickly called it.

Minutes later, he began to speak. 'Is that Snecksoft?' he said. 'I'd like to speak to Mr Sneck . . .'

OoOoO

Jake and Brigid went for lunch near the office.

'Again it's not dinner for two tonight,' Jake said. 'I'm sorry about that.'

'It doesn't matter,' said Brigid. 'Perhaps tomorrow night.'

Jake and Brigid talked about Al's dad, and about Al's plan to stay in America for some months.

'Perhaps I can stay and do Al's job here,' Jake finished. 'Al's OK with that. But what do you say?'

'It's a good plan, I think,' said Brigid, and she smiled.

Jake went back to his apartment. He worked on the racing game all afternoon. Then he put his laptop on the table near the window.

'I must give you some food before I go out, Percy,' he said.

'Food!' answered the parrot.

'Tonight I'm going to eat near the River Liffey,' said Jake. 'What do you think about that?'

mobile phone a phone that you can carry with you

'River Liffey!' squawked the parrot.

'And I'm going to see beautiful Brigid,' said Jake.

'Beautiful Brigid!' cried Percy.

Jake laughed. 'That's right!'

Tomás phoned at 6.30 p.m.

'I'm waiting in a taxi **outside** your apartment building, Jake,' he said. 'We're meeting everyone at the restaurant.'

'OK,' said Jake. 'I'm coming down now.'

Across the street and fifty metres away, Aidan watched Jake's apartment. He saw when the taxi arrived. Some minutes later, Jake came out of the apartment building and got into the taxi with Tomás. Then they drove away. Aidan saw all this.

He waited for two or three minutes. Then he walked across to the apartment building. He went up to Jake's apartment. He took out the key from his coat pocket and he opened the door. He went quietly into the apartment and he walked quickly across to the table and Jake's laptop. He put the laptop into a bag.

Suddenly, there was a loud 'Squawk!'

Aidan looked quickly across at Percy's cage. 'Be quiet, you **stupid** bird!' he said. 'What are you– ?'

Just then, he heard his mobile phone . . .

outside in front of a building

stupid not thinking well

READING CHECK

1 Match the two parts of the sentences.

a Erin and Oona give Jake

b Tomás gives Jake

c Brigid's present for Jake is

d Aidan gives Jake

1 a Dublin football shirt.

2 a beautiful hat.

3 an old photo of Dublin.

4 an old computer book.

2 Who says what? Match the people with what they say.

1 Be quiet.

2 ~~I didn't have any money for a present.~~

3 Is that Snecksoft?

4 I'm coming down now.

5 I'm waiting in a taxi.

6 It's a good plan, I think.

7 Perhaps I can stay and do Al's job here.

8 Squawk!

9 That isn't important.

a Aidan tells Jake, '...2...'

b Jake says to Aidan, '.........'

c Jake says to Brigid, '.........'

d Brigid tells Jake, '.........'

e '.........' asks Aidan by phone.

f Tomás tells Jake, '.........'

g Jake says to Tomás, '.........'

h Aidan tells Percy, '.........'

i '.........' answers Percy.

WORD WORK

1 Find five more words from Chapter 4 in the wordsquare.

M	O	V	L	O	D	S	H	K	C	S
T	O	W	P	K	I	E	U	D	K	N
G	U	B	R	R	L	G	V	A	E	U
V	T	D	I	U	P	S	I	L	S	J
E	S	U	Z	L	R	T	D	G	H	A
L	I	J	E	K	E	U	W	T	O	F
O	D	A	C	L	S	P	R	R	L	T
F	E	J	V	U	E	I	H	U	W	R
F	M	X	L	Z	N	D	I	O	I	I
Q	G	I	D	U	T	U	G	S	N	L
D	S	B	E	S	Y	H	Y	R	O	E

2 Use the words in Exercise 1 to complete the sentences.

a Aidan gives a birthday ...~~present~~... to Jake. It's an old computer book.

b Aidan goes into the street and phones Arto Sneck on his ....

c There's a .... for the best computer game at the Irish Computer Exhibition.

d BananaTech didn't .... a thing last year, but perhaps this year Jake's game is going to be the best in the exhibition.

e Aidan is waiting .... Jake's apartment when Jake leaves for the restaurant with Tomás.

f Aidan calls Percy a '.................. bird'.

GUESS WHAT

| Percy | Jake | Aidan | Brigid | Arto Sneck |

What happens in the next chapter? Complete each sentence with a name.

a .... calls Aidan with a place and a time to meet.

b .... takes the laptop with the game on it.

c .... can't find the laptop the next day.

d .... comes to the apartment and wants to help.

e .... says something important to Brigid.

CHAPTER 5 - HERBERT PARK

'Hello?' he said. 'Oh, yes, Mr Sneck . . . Yes, I've got it . . . What? . . . You want to meet tomorrow morning before the exhibition? . . . Yes, that's OK . . . But when and where? . . . Eight o'clock . . . by Herbert **Park** . . . Yes, OK. But please remember to bring the money . . . Goodbye, Mr Sneck.'

He put the phone back in his coat pocket. 'Eight o'clock, by Herbert Park,' he said to himself. 'Thank you, Mr Sneck. Now I'm going to be rich!'

He looked at the parrot. 'Did you hear that, you stupid bird?' he laughed. 'I'm going to be rich! I'm going to have lots of money! At eight o'clock, by Herbert Park!'

He looked at the nice things in the apartment. 'Perhaps Snecksoft can give me an apartment when I work for them,' he thought.

park a big garden that is open to everybody to visit

Aidan left the apartment quickly. Once he was down in the street again, he ran home with the bag.

OoOoO

Up in the apartment, Percy spoke some new **words**.

'Eight o'clock!' he cried. 'Herbert Park! Mr Sneck! Eight o'clock! Herbert Park! Mr Sneck!'

OoOoO

Jake was tired when they left the restaurant. He wanted to sleep. 'Saturday's going to be a busy day,' he thought.

When he arrived at the apartment, he walked over to Percy's cage. He didn't look for his laptop. He was tired but happy, and he didn't want to think about work. He had more interesting things – or a more interesting person – in his head – Brigid!

'I love Brigid!' he said.

'Love Brigid!' squawked Percy.

Jake laughed. 'Good night, Percy.'

OoOoO

At seven o'clock the next morning, Jake went to look for his laptop. Of course, it wasn't there. He ran quickly from room to room, but the laptop wasn't in the apartment. 'What am I going to do?' he cried. Just then, Brigid phoned. 'I'm waiting for you outside. Are you ready? Come down.'

'I can't, Brigid. Something bad happened last night.'

'Oh,' she said. 'I had a good time at the restaurant. The seafood was wonderful. '

'It's not about yesterday evening,' said Jake quickly. 'Someone **stole** my laptop when we were down by the river. I didn't learn about it last night because I was tired when I arrived home and went to bed at once. Can you come up to the apartment?'

word a thing that you say or write

steal (*past* **stole**) to take something without asking

Brigid went up. 'That's **strange**,' she thought. 'Did somebody **break in** here last night? There aren't any **signs** of it.' 'It's OK,' she told Jake. 'We can phone the **police** about your laptop, and we can phone Al and he can **send** your game **electronically** from San Francisco in time for the exhibition.'

'But I changed a lot of things on my laptop here,' said Jake. 'The game on my laptop is better.'

'Well, the laptop isn't here, so the game in San Francisco is better than nothing,' said Brigid. 'OK. It's quarter past seven in the morning here, so it's quarter past eleven at night in San Francisco. Let's phone him now.'

Jake phoned Al's house, but Al didn't answer. He phoned Al's mobile. Again, Al didn't answer. 'Perhaps he's at the hospital with his dad,' said Jake.

'Herbert Park!' squawked Percy.

'Be quiet, Percy!' said Jake. 'What are we going to do now, Brigid?'

'I'm going to phone the police,' said Brigid. 'You can phone Al again.'

strange not usual

break in (*past* **broke in**) to go into a place by breaking the door or window because you want to take something from it

sign something that shows you something important

police men and women who stop people doing bad things

send (*past* **sent**) to put into your computer for the Internet to take to a different computer

electronically using a computer

'Eight o'clock!' squawked Percy.

'Be quiet, Percy!' said Jake angrily. 'There's no answer at Al's house. And we need that game for the exhibition at nine o'clock.'

'Eight o'clock! Herbert Park!' squawked Percy.

Fifteen minutes later, Brigid finished her phone call. 'The police asked lots of questions,' she said. 'Did someone break in here? There aren't any signs of it. I told them about the key for this apartment in my desk. I need to find it, they say.'

'Eight o'clock! Herbert Park!' squawked Percy. Brigid suddenly looked at the parrot.

'Why is he saying that?' she asked.

'I don't know. Stupid bird. He's saying some new words now. He didn't stop talking all night. I heard him.'

'What new words?' asked Brigid. 'Do you want to say something, Percy?'

'Eight o'clock! Herbert Park! Mr Sneck! Going to be rich!'

'See?' said Jake. 'Stupid bird.'

READING CHECK

Correct ten more mistakes in the story.

Arto Sneck

~~Tomás O'Neill~~ phones Aidan and gives him a time and place to meet – nine o'clock by Herbert Park. Aidan leaves Jake's apartment with Jake's parrot in his bag and runs home. Jake comes home early from the restaurant and soon goes to bed. The next morning he looks for the bird in his apartment, but he can't find it. When Oona arrives, she phones the police. They ask her about the pizza for the apartment in her desk at the office. Jake phones Helsinki. He wants to speak to Al. Perhaps his friend can send the cage to him from there? But Al doesn't answer. Then Brigid listens carefully to Percy's old words. Perhaps the parrot wants to tell them nothing?

WORD WORK

Use the letters in the bag to make words and complete the sentences.

a Arto Sneck wants to meet Aidan by a ...... park ...... near the exhibition rooms.

b Percy learns some new .... from Aidan.

c 'Somebody .... my laptop last night!' Jake tells Brigid the next day.

d 'Did someone .... in here?' thinks Brigid.

e There are no .... of that in Jake's apartment.

f The windows and the door are OK. It is all very ...., Brigid feels.

g Brigid wants to phone the ....

h Perhaps Al can .... Jake's game to him from San Francisco.

i You can put pictures, videos, and games into a computer ....

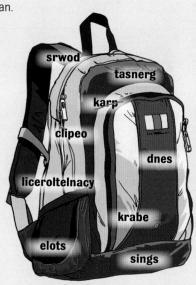

srwod
tasnerg
karp
clipeo
dnes
liceroltelnacy
krabe
elots
sings

GUESS WHAT

What happens in the last chapter? Tick one picture.

a Percy gets out of his cage and Jake runs after him to Herbert Park. ☐

c Jake and Brigid go and find Jake's laptop in Aidan's home. ☐

b Aidan gives Jake's laptop to Arto Sneck near Herbert Park. ☐

d Aidan gives Jake's laptop back and helps Jake with his presentation. ☐

CHAPTER 6 - DINNER FOR TWO

Brigid was quiet for a minute. Then she said, 'Those are strange words for a parrot. Where did Percy learn them?'

'Well, he didn't learn them from me,' said Jake. 'Perhaps he learnt them from Al.'

'Perhaps,' said Brigid, slowly. 'Or perhaps he learnt them when someone broke in here and stole your laptop. Perhaps he learnt those words from the **thief**!'

Jake looked at her. 'Yes!' he said. 'You're right! Percy usually says words soon after he hears them.'

'What did he say just then?' asked Brigid.

'"Eight o'clock, Herbert Park, Sneck, going to be rich", I think,' said Jake.

'Sneck!' said Brigid. 'Wait a minute! That's the name of Snecksoft's director!'

'Snecksoft?' said Jake. 'The Finnish computer company?'

'Yes!' said Brigid. 'Mr Sneck is going to be at the Computer Exhibition. Tell me again: what did Percy say?'

'He said, "Sneck, Herbert Park, eight o'clock",' answered Jake. 'Hey! That's a place and a time to meet!'

'So the thief is meeting Mr Sneck!' said Brigid.

'With my racing game!' cried Jake.

'We need to get to Herbert Park – fast,' said Brigid.

OoOoO

Aidan ran through the streets of Dublin to Herbert Park. Jake's laptop was in his bag. 'Soon I'm going to meet Mr Sneck, and he's going to give me a job,' he thought. 'I'm going to have lots more money, and I can help my mum to become well again.' Now he could see the park in front of him. But where was Mr Sneck? He could

thief (*plural* **thieves**) a person who takes things without asking

see nobody, but there was a big, black car in the road by the park.

Suddenly, three men got out of the car – Mr Sneck and two very big men in black suits. Aidan **crouched down** behind the car. Mr Sneck and the two men couldn't see him there.

'Where's the boy? He's late,' said one of the men.

'Yes,' said Mr Sneck. 'But he's going to come, I know. He wants money and a job at Snecksoft.'

'But he's a boy,' the second man in black said. 'Are you going to give him a job?'

'Of course not,' said Mr Sneck. 'But I didn't tell him that.' The three men laughed. Behind the car, Aidan felt ill. 'So, Mr Sneck **lied** to me. He never planned to give me a job,' he thought. 'And now I'm going to lose my job at BananaTech – and perhaps I'm going to go to **prison**. I need to stay very quiet here. I don't want to give Jake's laptop to Mr Sneck now.' Then suddenly he looked up. Mr Sneck stood in front of him, tall and angry.

crouch down to bend your legs and put your body near the ground

lie to say something that is not true

prison a place where people must stay when they do something wrong

'Why are you crouching down there, Aidan?' he said very coldly.

'I felt, erm, tired,' answered Aidan.

'Tired? Well, give that big bag to me then. One of my men can carry it for you,' said Mr Sneck. And the two men in black suits moved nearer. Aidan was afraid, but he said, 'No, I'm OK. You don't need to carry my bag. I can carry it. Erm, the thing is, I don't have the game with me. I came here to tell you that. I couldn't find it.'

'He's lying,' said one of the big men. 'He's got the game. He heard your words earlier and now he doesn't want to give it to us.' And he **pulled** Aidan to his feet. 'Give the bag to me now, or I'm going to hit you in the face.'

Just then, a woman behind Aidan spoke. 'Is there a problem?' she said. It was Brigid. Aidan looked quickly behind him. Jake and Brigid looked back at him. 'Thanks for bringing my things to the exhibition for me,' said Jake,

pull to move something quickly nearer you

and he took the bag quickly from Aidan. Mr Sneck and the two men in suits did not look happy, but in front of Jake and Brigid they could do nothing. 'Come on, Aidan,' said Brigid, and she pulled him to her. The three men got into their car and drove away.

'So, *you* were the thief,' said Jake. 'You took my laptop and you planned to give my game to Mr Sneck. Why?'

'I wanted a job with Snecksoft,' said Aidan unhappily. 'I love making computer games, and I needed money to help my mum. But nobody at BananaTech understands. For them I'm nothing more than a stupid coffee maker. But now you're going to call the police and they're going to put me in prison.'

'No, I'm not, Aidan,' said Jake. 'Listen. You're going to be a very good computer game writer one day. But you need someone to help you. I'd like to do that. But you must **promise** me something: you're never going to do a thing like this again. Do you promise?'

'Yes, I promise,' said Aidan. 'But are you truly going to help me?'

'Of course,' said Jake. 'But first you're going to help me. The exhibition begins in half an hour – and my presentation begins then too. You need to take that bag inside, find the BananaTech **exhibition stand** and make everything ready for me. Can you do that?'

'Yes!' said Aidan, and he ran.

OoOoO

More than four hundred people listened to Jake's presentation. They watched the racing game on a big screen. They listened to the music and sound effects. Then they clapped and shouted, 'It's wonderful!'

promise to say that you will certainly do something

exhibition stand a place where you put things for people to see

Everyone from the office came up and spoke to Jake after the presentation.

'You were very good,' said Oona.

'It was the best presentation at the Exhibition,' said Brigid.

'We're going to get the prize for 'Game of the Year', I think,' said Tomás happily.

One man did not clap after Jake's presentation. He stood next to the Snecksoft exhibition stand and he was very angry. Angry about Jake's wonderful game.

It was Mr Sneck.

That evening, Jake was very happy. 'Percy,' said Jake, 'it's dinner for two tonight!' Brigid arrived early. 'Come up,' said Jake, 'I must give some food to Percy before we go out.'

Brigid came in and went across to Percy's cage. 'You're a clever thing,' she said. 'We found Jake's game because you helped us.'

'And we stopped Aidan doing something very stupid, too,' said Jake.

'Something stupid!' squawked Percy.

'You're a very beautiful bird,' laughed Brigid.

'Beautiful Brigid! Love Brigid!' squawked Percy.

'Now where did he learn to say that?' she asked.

Jake's face was suddenly red. 'Er– I don't know,' he said.

'Yes, you do,' said Brigid, and she laughed. 'But it's OK. You're a nice man, Jake Stevens, and I like you. So let's go out and have some dinner.'

'Beautiful Brigid! Nice Jake! Dinner for two!' squawked Percy after they left.

READING CHECK

1 Are these sentences True or False? Tick the boxes

		True	False
a	Brigid listens to Percy the parrot's strange words.	☑	☐
b	'He learnt them from me,' says Jake.	☐	☐
c	'Tell me again: what did Percy say?' asks Brigid.	☐	☐
d	'That's a place and a time to meet,' says Percy.	☐	☐
e	Jake and Brigid need to go to Herbert Park for eight o'clock.	☐	☐

2 Put these sentences in the correct order. Number them 1–10.

a ☐ Aidan goes behind Arto Sneck's car.

b ☐ Aidan arrives at Herbert Park.

c ☐ Aidan tells Sneck, 'I don't have the game.'

d ☐ Aidan plans not to give the laptop to Sneck.

e ☐ Brigid and Jake arrive at Herbert Park.

f ☐ Jake takes the bag from Aidan.

g ☐ Mr Sneck and his men laugh about Aidan.

h ☐ One of Sneck's men tells Aidan, 'Give the bag to me.'

i ☐ Sneck and his men get into their car and drive away.

j ☐ Sneck finds Aidan behind his car.

Herbert Park

WORD WORK

Complete the sentences with the words in the car in the correct form.

pull · exhibition stand · lie · crouch · thief · promise · prison

a Sneck doesn't see Aidan at first because he ..*crouches*.. down behind the car.

b Aidan is .... to Sneck and his men when he says, 'I couldn't find the game.'

c Aidan doesn't want to go to ....

d He doesn't want to be a computer game .... for Sneck any more.

e One of Sneck's men .... Aidan to his feet.

f Jake .... to help Aidan.

g Aidan takes Jake's laptop inside to the BananaTech ....

GUESS WHAT

What happens after the story finishes? Choose from these ideas or add your own.

a ☐ Aidan begins writing wonderful computer games and makes lots of money.

b ☐ Tomás O'Neill says sorry to Aidan.

c ☐ A famous doctor helps Aidan's mother to become well again.

d ☐ Jake stays in Ireland with Brigid.

e ☐ Jake takes Brigid back to California with him.

f ☐ Brigid works at BananaTech California for a time.

g ☐ Al's father dies.

h ☐ Al goes to work for Snecksoft in Finland.

i ☐ Snecksoft loses lots of money.

j ☐ Arto Sneck stops making computer games.

k ☐ ....

l ☐ ....

Project A *Messages on Twitter*

What are you doing now?

People put short answers to this question on the Twitter website.

1 Read this Twitter Message (or 'tweet') from one of the people in *Jake's Parrot* and answer the questions below.

> I'm at Dublin airport with the BananaTech Ireland office manager. I have my bag and I'm waiting for a good friend from California to arrive.

a Who is the tweet from?

b Who is 'the BananaTech Ireland office manager'?

c Who is the 'good friend from California'?

d Which chapter of the story (and which pages, and which lines) is this message about?

e How many characters (letters, spaces and punctuation marks) are there in the tweet?

2 Now complete the tweets below and on page 41 with the phrases from the box. Who wrote each tweet?

apartment	changes	coffee	exhibition
game	mum	presentation	restaurant

a

> I'm making .... for everybody in the office. I'm angry with the boss. When can I begin working on computer games? I need money for my ....

Tweet is by: ....

b

> I'm watching Jake Stevens. Everyone is speaking to him after his .... at the exhibition. His new .... is wonderful. I feel very ill.

Tweet is by: ....

40

c I'm working at home. The .... is tomorrow and I must make some .... to the game before then. Percy is sleeping now – so it's quiet.

Tweet is by:..................

d We're coming back from the .... now. Everybody from the office is waiting for us in the .... Jake doesn't know this, but I know!

Tweet is by:..................

3 **Which part of the story are the tweets in Activity 2 about? Find the chapter, the page(s), and the lines.**

Tweet	Chapter	Page(s)	Lines
a			
b			
c			
d			

4 **Write a tweet from a story character about a different part of the story. Can your classmates find the character and the part of the story?**

Project B *A famous river*

1 Read the text about the River Liffey and complete the table below.

IRELAND

Dublin

Shannon
Limerick

Waterford

Cork

The River Liffey is a river in Ireland. It goes through the centre of the city of Dublin. The name comes from the flat land around the river, and this takes its name from Aife, a famous fighting woman from Ireland long ago. 'Aife' means 'beautiful' in Gaelic. The river is 125 kilometres long. It begins in the Wicklow mountains and flows through the counties of Wicklow, Kildare and Dublin, before its waters go into the Irish sea in Dublin Bay. The earliest stone bridge over the River Liffey was built in 1488. These days you can take a tour of Dublin by river on a 50-seat water taxi.

What's the name of the river?	
Which country is it in?	
Which city does it go through?	
Where does the name of the river come from?	
How long is it?	
Where does it begin?	
Which counties does it flow through?	
Where do its waters go?	
What do we know about the history of the river?	
What can you do there these days?	

2 Use the notes in the table to complete the text about the Sacramento River below.

What's the name of the river?	The Sacramento River
Which country is it in?	the United States
Which cities does it go through?	Redding, Colusa, Sacramento, Rio Vista
Where does the name of the river come from?	'Sacramento' ('Holy Sacrament' in Spanish) because it was very beautiful
How long is it?	640 kilometres
Where does it begin?	the Klamath Mountains
Which state does it flow through?	California
Where do its waters go?	into the San Francisco Bay
What do we know about the history of the river?	Gabriel Moraga was the first European to see (and name) the river in 1808
What can you do there these days?	go fishing, boating or waterskiing; and walking or camping

The .... River is a river in .... It goes through the cities of ...., ..., ..., and .... The name means '...............' in .... The river is .... kilometres long. It begins in the .... and flows through the American State of .... before its waters go into the .... The Spanish explorer .... was the first .... to see (and name) the river in the year .... These days you can go ...., ... or .... in the river and .... or .... by it.

CALIFORNIA — Sacramento, San Francisco, San Jose, Los Angeles, San Diego

3 **Use the notes in the table to write a text about the River Torne.**

What's the name of the river?	The River Torne
Which countries is it in?	Sweden and Finland
Which twin city does it go through?	Haparanda/Tornio (in Sweden/Finland)
What does the name of the river mean?	Torne comes from old Finnish. It means 'spear'
How long is it?	522 kilometres
Where does it begin?	Lake Torne in Sweden
Which provinces does it flow through, and by?	Norbotten (Sweden) Lapland (Finland)
Where do its waters go?	into the Gulf of Bothnia
What do you know about the history of the river?	in 1809, the lower Torne became the Swedish border with Finland (then part of Russia)
What can you do there these days?	see the Ice Hotel in Jukkasjärvi, Sweden (made from the Torne's waters in winter); ride a snowmobile; fish

4 **Choose another famous river. Find out information about it on the Internet. Write a short text about it.**

Amazon Danube Ganges
Mississippi NILE Yangtze

GRAMMAR CHECK

Verb + infinitive or –ing form verb

Some verbs, like *begin, forget, learn, need, remember, want* and *would like* are followed by **to + infinitive**.

Al needs to go and see his dad in hospital.

Remember to give him food and water every day!

Some verbs, like *begin, go, finish, like, love* and *stop* are followed by the **–ing** form of the verb.

Jake doesn't like leaving California.

He loves meeting Brigid.

1 Choose the correct word or words to complete the sentences.

a Al forgets *telling/to tell* Jake about his father before they meet.

b Jake stops *to look/looking* happily at Brigid when he sees Al's bag.

c Jake would like *going/to go* to dinner with Brigid.

d Al doesn't want *to leave/leaving* Percy in Ireland.

e Percy is learning *to speak/speaking* from Al.

2 Complete the sentences. Use the infinitive or –ing form of the verbs in brackets.

a Brigid doesn't forget ...*to give*... (give) the key to the apartment to Jake.

b Jake goes .... (walk) over to the window.

c He stops .... (look) out at the sea when he hears a squawk behind him.

d Percy begins .... (talk) when Brigid talks to him.

e Jake needs .... (give) Percy some food and water every day.

f Jake would like .... (take) Brigid out to dinner.

g Brigid doesn't want .... (have) dinner with Jake on his first night in Dublin.

h Al remembered .... (leave) some food for Jake in the apartment.

i Jake finishes .... (give) food and water to Percy and then he has his dinner.

j Percy loves .... (speak) when nobody is listening.

GRAMMAR CHECK

Present Simple: Yes/No questions and short answers

We use is/are or the auxiliary verbs do/does and can + infinitive without *to* in Yes/No questions in the Present Simple.

Does Aidan like working here?   Can you help him?

Is it going to be the best game at the Irish Computer Exhibition?

In the short answer, we repeat the subject and re-use the auxiliary verb **or is/are.**

No, he doesn't.   Yes, I can.

Yes, it is.

3 Write answers for the questions about Aidan. Use the short answers in the box.

No, he can't.	No, he doesn't.	No, they don't.	~~No, he isn't.~~
No, there isn't.	Yes, he does.	Yes, he is.	Yes, she is. Yes, they do.

a Is Tomás nice to Aidan? ..No, he isn't........

b Does Aidan smile very much? ....

c Is he always angry? ....

d Does he want to work on computer games? ....

e Is there somebody in the office to help him? ....

f Can he work on computer games now? ....

g Is Aidan's mother very ill? ....

h Do Aidan's family have a lot of money? ....

i Do they live near the airport? ....

4 Write short answers for these questions about Al.

a Is Al from Ireland? ...No, he isn't.......

b Is his father badly ill? ....

c Does Al have brothers and sisters? ....

d Is his mother dead? ....

e Can Al come back to Ireland at once? ....

GRAMMAR CHECK

Going to Future: affirmative and negative

We make the *going to* future with the verb be (not) + going to + infinitive. We use the *going to* future for plans, intentions, and predictions with evidence now.

I'm going to have dinner at my mum's house. (plan)

I'm not going to make coffee for any of them again. (intention)

This is going to be my best birthday. (prediction)

5 **What is going to happen in the story? Put the words in order and write sentences.**

a Arto Sneck / to phone / Aidan / is going

Aidan is going to phone Arto Sneck.

b at the / Arto Sneck / to be / is going / Computer Exhibition

....

c computer games / is going / Aidan / to make

....

d isn't / Jake / going to / a birthday / have / dinner for two

....

e Brigid / isn't going / dinner with / to bring / Jake / her mother to

....

f is going / Jake's apartment / to wait / Everybody / in

....

g They're / 'Happy Birthday' / all / sing / going to

....

h lots of / to have / going / fun / Everyone's

....

i to remember / a night / to be / It's going

....

GRAMMAR CHECK

Linkers: so and because

We use so to link two sentences when the second sentence explains a result.

It's Jake's birthday so the people from the office give him presents

(= result of first part of sentence)

We use because to link two sentences when the second sentence explains a reason.

Aidan doesn't eat because he's looking at Jake's laptop.

(= result of first part of sentence)

6 **Match a–g with 1–7. Write complete sentences using *so* or *because*.**

a Jake likes computers…

Jake likes computers so Aidan gives him a computer book.

b Aidan gives an old book to Jake…

....

c The book is very good…

....

d Everybody goes to work early the next day…

....

e Tomás wants to thank people…

....

f Jake wants to work on his game at home…

....

g Aidan takes the key from Brigid's desk…

....

1 ~~Aidan gives him a computer book.~~

2 he doesn't have money for a new present.

3 he takes them all to dinner.

4 he wants to visit Jake's apartment later.

5 it's quieter there.

6 Jake thanks Aidan very warmly for it.

7 they have lots to do.

GRAMMAR CHECK

Adverbs of manner

We use adverbs of manner to talk about how we do things.

He ran quickly from room to room.

'Be quiet, Percy!' said Jake angrily.

We make adverbs from adjectives by adding –ly.

quick – quickly

For adjectives that end in –y, we change y to –ily.

angry – angrily

Some adverbs are irregular.

fast – fast   good – well

7 Write the adverbs of these adjectives.

a strange ...*strangely*..

b quick ....

c tired ....

d happy ....

e good ....

f noisy ....

g sudden ....

h careful ....

8 Complete each sentences using an adverb from Exercise 7.

a 'I love Brigid!' Jake tells Percy ......*happily*...... .

b Jake doesn't do any more work that night, but goes to bed ....

c Jake sleeps very .... , and he gets up early the next morning.

d Brigid comes up to his apartment .... when Jake tells her, 'Somebody stole my laptop last night.'

e .... there are no signs in Jake's apartment of somebody breaking in.

f 'Eight o'clock! Herbert Park!' squawks Percy ....

g Jake doesn't listen to Percy's words very ....

h Brigid .... looks at the parrot.

GRAMMAR CHECK

Information questions with question words

We use question words – like *how, who, what, why, where* and *when* – in information questions. We answer these questions by giving some information.

Where does Aidan meet Mr Sneck? At Herbert Park.

Question words go at the beginning of a question. When the question word is the object of the question, we use an auxiliary verb before the subject.

What time does he go there?

When did he leave Jake's apartment.

After the auxiliary verb *do/does* or *did*, we use infinitive without *to*.

How many people does Mr Sneck have with him?

9 **Complete each question to Mr Sneck using the correct question word: *how, what, why, when, where, which, who,* or *why*. Then match your questions with his answers.**

a .....What..... do your friends call you? ⬚8

b .... country do you come from? ⬚

c .... city do you usually live in? ⬚

d .... did Snecksoft last win the 'Game of the Year' prize? ⬚

e .... did you want to steal Jake Stevens's car racing game? ⬚

f .... is the Snecksoft game about this year? ⬚

g .... did you promise to give Aidan for his help? ⬚

h .... did you plan to meet Aidan? ⬚

i .... many men did you take with you? ⬚

j .... did you and your men drive away without the game? ⬚

k .... did you feel when you saw Jake Stevens's presentation? ⬚

1 A job at Snecksoft.

2 In Herbert Park.

3 Because it's better than the Snecksoft game this year.

4 Because Jake Stevens and a woman from BananaTech suddenly arrived.

5 It's a football game.

6 Helsinki.

7 Angry.

8 Arto.

9 Finland.

10 Last year.

11 Two.

GRAMMAR CHECK

Present Continuous

We use the Present Continuous to talk about things happening now or around now.

We make the Present Continuous with the verb be + the –ing form of the verb.

Brigid's wearing a nice blue dress.

When short verbs end in a consonant + vowel + consonant, we double the final consonant and add –ing.

sit – Jake's sitting at his desk.

When verbs end in consonant + e, we remove the e and add –ing.

make – He's making a lot of money.

We put n't (not) with the verb be to make the Present Continuous negative.

Percy isn't talking much today.

10 Complete the text with the Present Continuous form of the verbs in brackets.

Jake Stevens **a)** .....is living.... (live) in Ireland now. He **b)** .... (write) computer games and he **c)** .... (love) every minute of his time in Dublin with Brigid. His friend Al **d)** .... (stay) in California for some months to be with his father. His dad **e)** .... (begin) to feel better, and Al

f) .... (plan) to come back to Ireland when his father is out of hospital.

Aidan **g)** .... (work) on computer games at BananaTech now.

He **h)** .... (not make) coffee or tea for people in the office any more.

Tomás O'Neill **i)** .... (be) a lot nicer to him. That's because BananaTech

j) .... (do) very well. Jake and Aidan's new computer games

k) .... (win) prizes in lots of different countries these days.

Michael and Erin **l)** .... (not work) for BananaTech now. They

m) .... (run) a new computer game company 'Fun Games'.

Arto Sneck **n)** .... (not make) computer games any more, and Snecksoft

o) .... (lose) money.

DOMINOES Your Choice

Read *Dominoes* for pleasure, or to develop language skills. It's your choice.

Each *Domino* reader includes:
- a good story to enjoy
- integrated activities to develop reading skills and increase vocabulary
- task-based projects – perfect for CEFR portfolios
- contextualized grammar activities

Each *Domino* pack contains a reader, and an excitingly dramatized audio recording of the story

If you liked this *Domino*, read these:

Studio Five
Anthony Manning

Fay loves making The Friends' Hour for Studio Five, but her boss – Jason – is always angry with her. One day, a young man – Simon Jones – phones her show. Soon Fay must find Simon, and work hard to keep her job. Then her best friend – Wing –stops helping her. What can Fay do now? Can she and Wing stay friends?

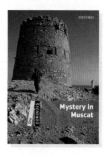

Mystery in Muscat
Julie Till

'How long is she in Oman for?'

'Ten days. And then they want to take her back home.'

'Ah, yes. But she's not going back to London. They're never going to see her again!'

Jamie and Taymour overhear this strange conversation near their homes in Muscat. Two men want to kill an important visitor, it seems. But who is the woman in danger? And what can the boys do to save her?

Can they, their sisters Sarah and Nadine, and their Australian friend Ruth find the answer to the mystery?

	CEFR	Cambridge Exams	IELTS	TOEFL iBT	TOEIC
Level 3	B1	PET	4.0	57-86	550
Level 2	A2–B1	KET-PET	3.0-4.0	–	390
Level 1	A1–A2	YLE Flyers/KET	3.0	–	225
Starter & Quick Starter	A1	YLE Movers	1.0–2.0	–	–

You can find details and a full list of books and teachers' resources on our website:
www.oup.com/elt/gradedreaders